Specimen Sight-Reading Tests for Trumpet and Brass Band instruments 𝄞

(excluding Trombone 𝄞)

Trumpet, Cornet, Flugelhorn, E♭ Horn, Baritone 𝄞, Euphonium 𝄞, Tuba 𝄞

Grades 6-8

The Associated Board of
the Royal Schools of Music

Allegro non troppo
1
f
p
f
p
f
Moderato
2
f
p
f
p
Cantabile
3
mf
p cresc.
f
p
Moderato
4
f
p
f
p
p

Allegro
5
p
p
cresc.
f
Alla marcia
6
mp
mf
mp
f
p
f
Lento
7
p
mf
p
p
Andante
8
p
f
p
p
f
p
f

Allegro
9
f
p
f
p
cresc.
f
Maestoso
10
f
mp
mf
f
p
f
Andante
11
p
f
p
f
p
Grazioso
12
mf
p
f
p

Vivo
13
mf
f
p
f
p
f
Largo
14
mf
mf
p
f
rall.
p
Maestoso
15
f
p
f
p
Alla breve
16
f
p
f
p

Andante
17
f
p
f
p
f
p
Ritmico
18
f
f
f
p
f
f
f
Giocoso
19
mf
f
p
mf
p
Andante
20
mf
p
mf
f

Ritmico
1
f
p
cresc.
f
p
cresc.
f
p
Lento
2
mf
f
p
f
p
Moderato
3
mp
mf
mp
f
dim.
p
f
Moderato
4
mf
p
tr
p

5
Waltz
mf
f
p
f
p
f
p
6
Andante
p
mf
p
3
p
f
p
7
Moderato
f
p
cresc.
f
mp
f
p
f

Allegro assai
8
mp
f
mp
f
p
Alla marcia
9
p
f
p
Andante
10
mp
mf
f
p
Alla marcia
11
mf
f
mp
f
p
cresc.
tr
f

Moderato
12
f
p
mf
p
Andante
13
p
f
mp
f
p
f
p
Lento
14
p
f
dim.
p
f
mf
p
Andante
15
mp
f
p
mf
p

Andante
1
mf
rall.
p
Vivace
2
f
p
f
p
f
p
f
p
cresc.
f
Ritmico
3
f
p
cresc.
f
p
cresc.
mf
p
cresc.
f

Moderato
4
mf
p
f
mp
p
f
p
f
Andante
5
mf
tr
p
f
f
Lento
6
mf
p
mp
mf
p
f

7
Maestoso
f
p
f
p
f
p cresc.
f
p sub.
f
8
Andantino
mp
p
cresc.
dim.
tr
p
cresc.
f
p
9
Vivo
f
p
cresc.
f
p
f
p
f
fp
f

Cantabile
1
cresc.
Alla marcia
2
Moderato
3
Moderato
4

Maestoso
5
f
mp
mf
f
p
f
Allegro non troppo
6
f
p
f
p
f
Alla marcia
7
mp
f
mp
f
p
cresc.
f
Grazioso
8
mf
p
f
p

Allegro
9
p
p
cresc.
f
Lento
10
p
f
dim.
p
f
mf
p
Scherzando
11
mp
mf
mp
f
p
f
Waltz
12
mp
mf
mp
f

Vivo
13
mf
f
p
f
Andante
14
f
p
f
p
f
p
Allegro
15
p
f
p
f
p
f
Moderato
16
p
f
p
cresc.
f

Grazioso
17
mf
p
f
p
Andantino
18
p
f
p
f
p
Lento
19
p
f
p
p
Maestoso
20
f
p
f
p

Waltz
1
mf
f
p
f
p
f
p
Ritmico
2
f
p cresc.
f
p
cresc.
mf
p
cresc.
f
ff
Lento
3
mf
p
mp
mf
p
f

4
Andante
p
f
mp
f
p
f
p
5
Andante
mf
p
f
p
6
Andante
p
f
p
p
f
p
p

Andante
7
mp
f
p
mf
p
Allegro
8
f
p
f
p
cresc.
f
Andante
9
p
mf
p
3
p
f
p

Moderato
1
mf
p
f
mf
p
f
p
f
Lento
2
mf
f
p
f
p
Moderato
3
f
p
cresc.
f
mp
f
p
f

Vivace
4
cresc.
Moderato
5
Moderato
6

Printed and bound in Great Britain by Caligraving Limited

2:06